Thank You So Much, For Purchasing With Us. Enjoy!

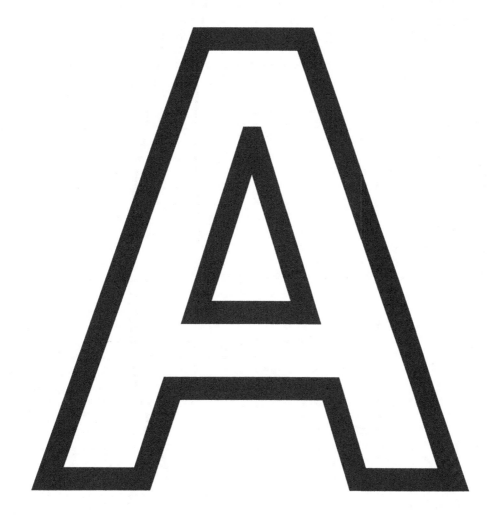

APATOSAURUS

- **_Apatosaurus:_** Known for its long neck and whip-like tail, Apatosaurus roamed the Late Jurassic landscape as one of the largest herbivores.

BRACHIOSAURUS

- **<u>Brachiosaurus</u>:** A towering giant of the Late Jurassic period, Brachiosaurus possessed an elongated neck and front legs, giving it a distinctive appearance.

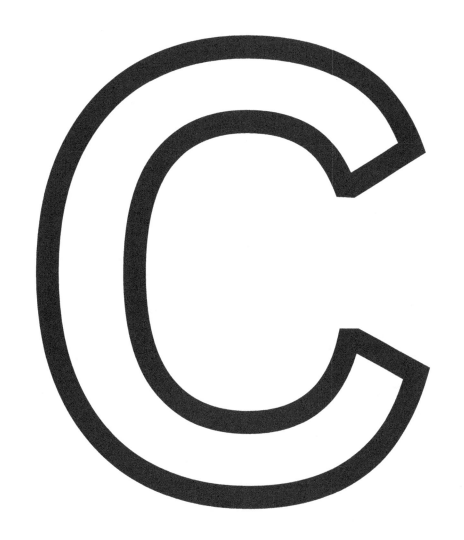

CARNOTAURUS

- **Carnotaurus**: Sporting diminutive arms and horns above its eyes, Carnotaurus was a fearsome predator of the Late Cretaceous known for its unusual appearance.

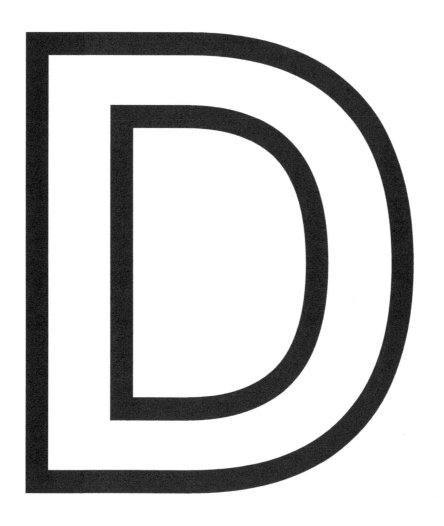

DILOPHOSAURUS

- **<u>Dilophosaurus</u>**: Recognizable by its dual crests atop its head, Dilophosaurus was an early Jurassic predator with a unique and striking appearance.

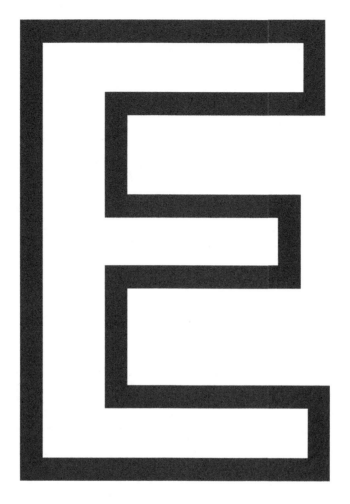

EDMONTOSAURUS

- **<u>Edmontosaurus</u>**. A dinosaur of the Late Cretaceous, Edmontosaurus was a large herbivore known for its extensive fossil record.

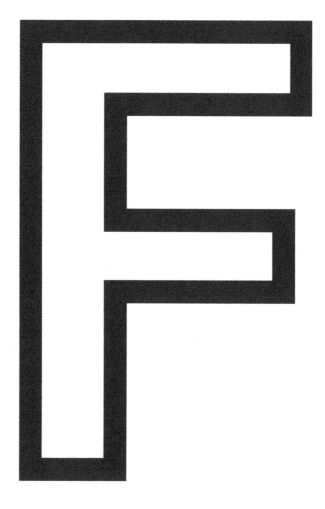

FABROSAURUS

(FICTIONAL)

- <u>**Fabrosaurus**</u> *Residing in the lush landscapes of the Late Cretaceous, this majestic herbivore navigated its environment with poise and resilience, leaving behind a legacy etched in the annals of paleontological discovery.*

GALLIMIMUS

- **_Gallimimus_**: Resembling an oversized ostrich, Gallimimus was a fleet-footed dinosaur of the Late Cretaceous known for its speed and agility.

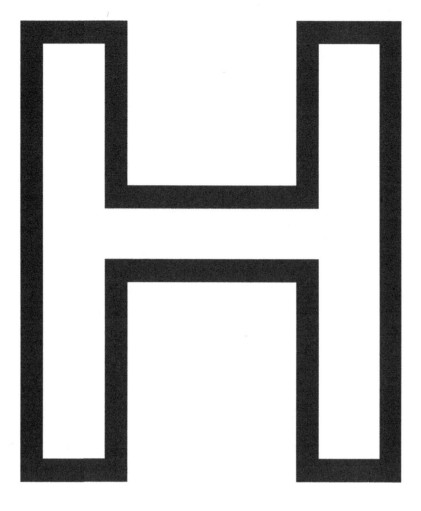

HADROSAURUS

Hadrosaurus Roaming the ancient landscapes during the Late Cretaceous period, this herbivorous giant captivates with its distinctive duck-billed snout, well-suited for grazing on vegetation that blanketed the prehistoric world.

IGUANODON

<u>Iguanodon:</u> Named for its iguana-like teeth, Iguanodon was an iconic herbivore of the Early Cretaceous known for its thumb spike.

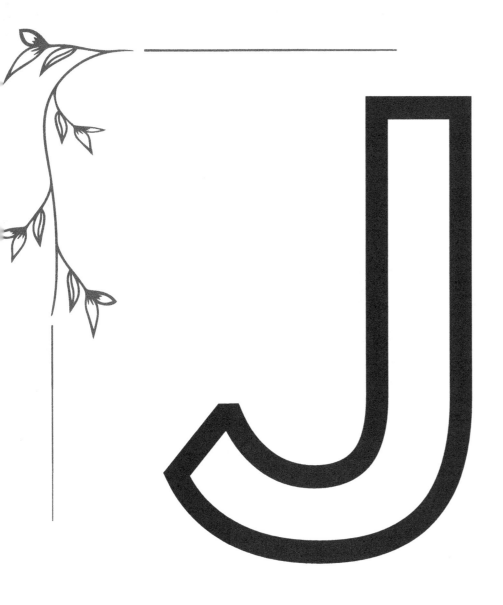

JURRASSOSAURUS
(FICTIONAL)

Jurrassosaurus (fictional): A creation of imagination blending the allure of the Jurassic era with the fantastical realm of fiction.

KENTROSAURUS

Kentrosaurus: Armored with rows of sharp spikes along its back and tail, Kentrosaurus was a stegosaurid dinosaur of the Late Jurassic.

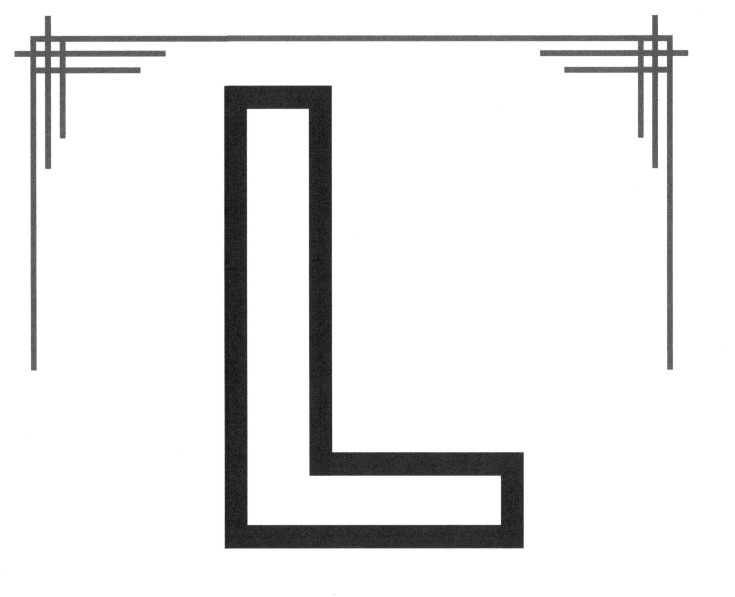

LAMBEOSAURUS

Lambeosaurus: Distinguished by its elaborate crest resembling a hatchet, Lambeosaurus was a duck-billed dinosaur of the Late Cretaceous.

M

MICRORAPTOR

Microraptor: A small, feathered dinosaur of the Early Cretaceous, Microraptor was equipped with flight feathers on both its arms and legs.

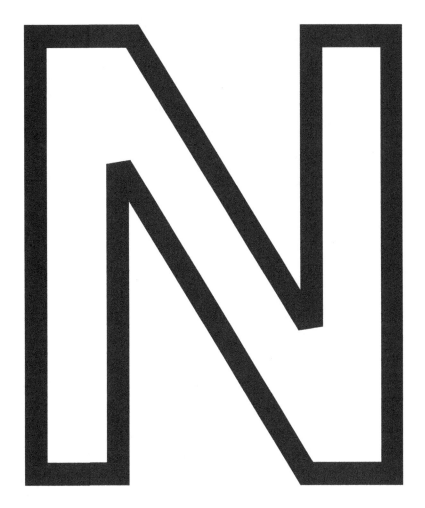

NODOSAURUS

<u>Nodosaurus</u>: Covered in bony plates called osteoderms, Nodosaurus was a nodosaurid dinosaur of the Late Cretaceous known for its defensive armor.

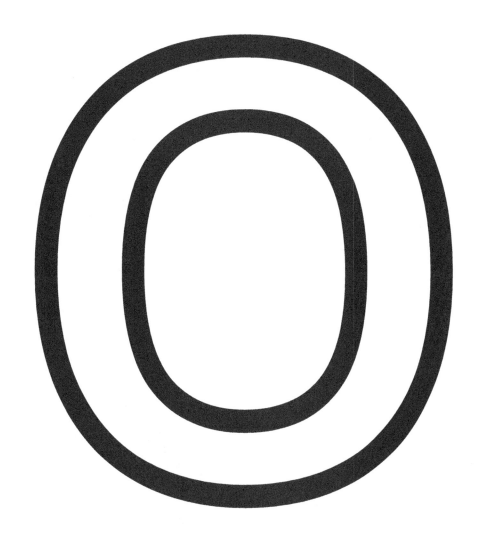

OVIRAPTOR

Oviraptor: Initially misunderstood as an egg thief, Oviraptor was later recognized as a dinosaur of the Late Cretaceous likely caring for its own eggs.

PARASAUROLOPHUS

Parasaurolophus was a dinosaur with a long, distinctive head crest. It lived in what is now North America during the Late Cretaceous Period.

QUETZALCOATLUS

Quetzalcoatlus is noted for its gigantic appearance. It had long, elongated neck; stork-like toothed jaws; and sharp, long and pointed beak.

RAPTOREX

Raptorex: A smaller precursor to the famous Tyrannosaurus rex, Raptorex was a carnivorous dinosaur of the Late Cretaceous known for its sharp teeth and powerful jaws.

STEGOSAURUS

<u>Stegosaurus</u>: Iconic for the plates along its back and the spikes on its tail, Stegosaurus was a herbivorous dinosaur of the Late Jurassic.

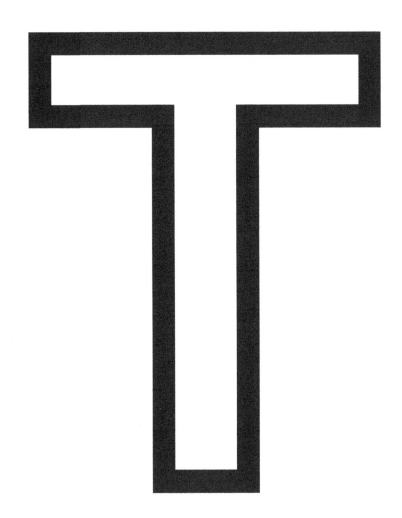

TRICERATOPS

Triceratops: Renowned for its three facial horns and frill adorned with bony ornaments, Triceratops was a horned dinosaur of the Late Cretaceous.

UNENLAGIA

<u>_Unenlagia_</u> is known as the most bird-like of all the dromaeosaurs. Despite that fact that Unenlagia had flight feathers and extremely flexible shoulders, both characteristics of flying animals, it is unlikely that this theropod could take flight because of its size.

VELOCIRAPTOR

Velociraptor: Made famous by popular culture, Velociraptor was a dromaeosaurid dinosaur of the Late Cretaceous, known for its predatory prowess and distinctive sickle-shaped claw

WANNANOSAURUS

Wannanosaurus (fictional): Invoking the intrigue of fictional worlds in a prehistoric era.

XENOCERATOPS

Xenoceratops (fictional): Stirring the imagination with its exotic name, Xenoceratops evokes images of a fantastical prehistoric creature.

YANGCHUANOSAURUS

<u>Yangchuanosaurus</u> was a large, powerful meat-eater. It walked on two large, muscular legs, had short arms, a strong, short neck, a big head with powerful jaws, and large, serrated teeth.

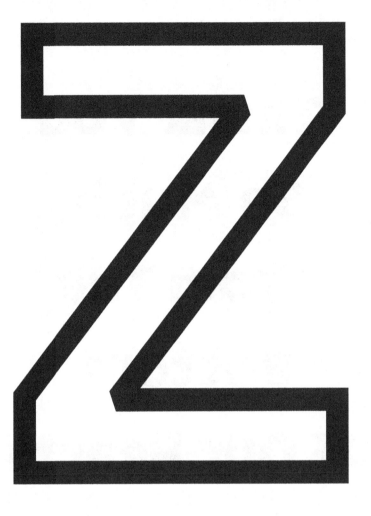

ZALMOXES

Zalmoxes dinosaur which typically walked on two legs and had distinguishing Characteristics like Narrow beak; slightly pointed skull and three toed feet

Thank You So Much, From The Bottom Of Our Hearts, We Wish You All The Very Best.

Made in the USA
Coppell, TX
13 December 2024